Oxford University Press
Walton Street Oxford OX2 6DP

LONDON   GLASGOW   NEW YORK
TORONTO   DELHI   BOMBAY
CALCUTTA   MADRAS   KARACHI
NAIROBI   DAR ES SALAAM
CAPE TOWN   SALISBURY
KUALA LUMPUR   SINGAPORE
HONG KONG   TOKYO   MELBOURNE
AUCKLAND

and associates in
BEIRUT   BERLIN   IBADAN
MEXICO CITY   NICOSIA

ISBN 019 834732 4
© D. A. Holland, S. A. Soper 1980
First published 1980
Reprinted 1982

Printed by The Blackmore Press,
Shaftesbury, Dorset

Problems 2

D. A. Holland
S. A. Soper

Oxford University Press

Contents

page 3   Number
page 8   Money
page 13   Time
page 18   Length
page 23   Weight
page 28   Capacity

Introduction

Word sums
Problems books 1, 2 and 3

Aims
1   To help the child to read, to understand, and to solve simple arithmetical problems.

2   To save time in the classroom by arranging material in graded examples for ease of use and continuity of method.

Structure
Word sums gives practice in working arithmetical questions set out in short phrases and in translating between words and symbols. It thus provides an introduction to the problems books, and it is also a useful aid to spelling.

The three problems books cover number, money, time, length, weight, capacity, simple fractions, decimals, and percentage. The careful grading takes account of difficulties in vocabulary, in comprehension, and in arithmetic. The wording of the questions aims for accuracy through the use of natural language that avoids ambiguity.

Use
These four books will be a useful supplement to any mathematics scheme since regular practice of reading and of the basic rules of arithmetic form an essential part of all courses at this level. Because the examples are graded and divided by pages into topics, it is a simple matter to isolate difficulties, to provide a controlled progression of work for each child, and to keep a record of individual progress.

Correction To simplify marking and analysis of errors, the layout of answer book and pupil's book is the same and where appropriate, children may correct their own answers.

78
3 4

Number
addition

1 Jo's stamp album contained 50 stamps, Jerry's 28 and Pam's 34. How many stamps did the children have between them?

2 500, 1000, 46, 360, 2640 Add the largest of these numbers to the smallest.

3 Owen's team has 80 points. The team gains 15 more for winning a race and 15 for tidiness. How many points has the team now?

4 A book contains 18 picture pages, 22 pages of words and 8 other pages. How many pages is this altogether?

5 Jim had 15 marbles in his pocket, 34 in his desk and 45 at home. How many marbles had he altogether?

6 Mr Green had 144 trees in his orchard. Last winter he planted 48 plum trees and 85 apple trees. What is the total number of trees in the orchard now?

7 A farmer bought 34 cows, 36 pigs and 48 sheep. How many animals did he buy altogether?

8 In spring we had about 130 daffodils, 140 tulips and 250 primroses blooming in our garden. About how many flowers is that altogether?

9 The village of South Dell had a population of 628. North Dell village had a population of 555. What was the combined population of the two villages?

Number
subtraction

1 In a box of 50 coloured pencils, 22 were broken. How many were not broken?

2 There were 14 boys in a class of 26 children. How many girls were in the class?

3 John had 30 marbles. After playing two games, he had lost 14. How many marbles did he have left?

4 Simon has 98 stamps in his album: this is 24 more than Martin. How many stamps has Martin?

5 I have read 28 pages of my 64-page book. How many pages are left to read?

6 An aeroplane can carry 120 passengers. If there are 30 empty seats, how many passengers are on board?

7 A farmer sold 45 cows from his herd of 160. How many cows remained?

8 The school ordered 240 bottles of milk. When the van delivered the milk, 23 bottles were missing. How many bottles were delivered?

9 In a crate of 150 apples, 38 were not yet ripe. How many apples were ripe?

Number
multiplication

1 Tim delivers 25 newspapers every morning except Sunday. How many does he deliver each week?

2 There are six tulips in a bunch. How many tulips would be needed to make 10 bunches?

3 Eight children are each given a box of 20 counters. How many counters are given altogether?

4 40, 10, 3, 25, 65 Multiply the largest number by the smallest.

5 There are 28 chairs in a classroom. How many chair legs will there be?

6 A clock strikes four times every hour. How often will it strike in 24 hours?

7 Six coaches each brought 44 supporters to the match. How many supporters is that?

8 Each child in a class of 26 was given four books. How many books were given out to the class?

9 How many legs are needed to make 20 three-legged stools?

Number
division

1 Forty-eight children were divided into 6 teams. How many children were in each team?

2 Five hundred daffodils were made into bunches of ten. How many bunches were made altogether?

3 One hundred apples in a box were divided equally into 25 bags. How many apples were in each bag?

4 Mother put 56 socks in the laundry bag. How many pairs is that?

5 Six hundred pencils were tied into bundles of five. How many bundles were made?

6 If 160 marbles are shared equally between 8 boys, how many marbles will each boy have?

7 Thirty trees were planted in rows of 6. How many rows of trees were planted?

8 40, 2, 1240, 300, 690 Divide the greatest of these numbers by the smallest.

9 Fred gave one-quarter of his 240 marbles to his brother in exchange for a fishing rod. How many marbles did Fred give?

Number
mixed

1 A train can seat 30 passengers in each of its 4 carriages. If half the seats are empty, how many passengers are on the train?

2 In a class of 36 children, 4 of them were absent. The rest were asked to form groups of four. How many groups could they make?

3 Tom scored 20 points. Bill scored twice as many. How many points did they score altogether?

4 100, 24, 30, 8, 3 Halve the highest number, then multiply your answer by the smallest number.

5 I counted 40 animals in a field. If 20 were cows, 10 were sheep and the rest were horses, how many horses were there?

6 James had 40 marbles. He put 10 in his pocket and shared the rest equally with Jason. How many marbles did he give to Jason?

7 There are seats on a bus for 24 passengers upstairs and 30 downstairs. How many passengers are on the bus when it is half full?

8 There are 30 cars in the yard and half of them each need four new tyres. How many new tyres are needed?

9 One-quarter of Jane's 400 beads are divided equally into 2 boxes. How many beads are put into each box?

Money
addition

1 Mother spent £1.50 on vegetables and 75p on fruit. How much did she spend altogether?

2 In my purse I have a fifty, 4 tens, 3 fives and a two. How much money is in my purse?

3 The collection amounted to £15.40. Miss Brown added 40p and Sam added 20p. What was the new total?

4 Jill's mother bought a new blouse costing £4.99, new socks for 86p, and a new skirt costing £6.00. How much did she pay altogether?

5 The teacher collected £9.60 in dinner money. John came late with his 80p. What was the final total of dinner money?

6 Three classes sent money for the school photograph to the office. Class 1 sent £3.40, Class 2 £5.60, Class 3 £6.20. How much money was sent altogether?

7 John has saved £3.85. He is given £1.40 for his birthday. How much money has he now?

8 £40, 40p, 68p, £65, £61.50, 49p Add the greatest amount to the smallest.

9 The weekly rent of £6.45 was increased by £1.20 What is the new weekly rent?

Money
subtraction

1 Martin borrows 40p from the £1.20 in the cash tin. How much money is left in the tin?

2 George gave a five pound note to pay for his track suit. If it cost £3.20, how much change should he have been given?

3 I spent £2.60 of my £6.00 holiday money on presents. How much money did I have left?

4 Simon saved £3.90 in his money box. How much more money must he save in order to buy a game costing £4.50?

5 The fare to Bedford is £1.80 and the fare to Luton is £3.00. How much more does it cost to travel to Luton?

6 Margaret collected £4.60 and Claire collected £3.90 for the Save the Children Fund. How much more money did Margaret collect?

7 £20, £120, £87, 20p, £10 Take the smallest amount from the greatest.

8 A £6 hat was reduced by £1.40 in the sales. What was the sale price of the hat?

9 Father's car cost £400 less than Uncle Jack's. If Uncle Jack's car cost £2000, how much did Father's cost?

Money
multiplication

1 My comic costs 12p each week. How much must I pay for the comic over 10 weeks?

2 Each of 6 children paid 80p for a train ticket. How much did they pay altogether?

3 Oranges cost 9p each. A shopkeeper sold 30 in a morning. How much did he collect for the oranges?

4 Four children each saved £1.60 for a trip. How much did they save between them?

5 Pansy plants cost 9p each. How much money must I pay if I buy one hundred pansy plants?

6 The price for printing is 13p a letter. Work out the cost of printing the name JOHN WRIGHT

7 A bag of fifty 10p coins was exchanged for pennies. How many pennies were given in exchange?

8 Tickets for the coach trip cost £1.50 each. How much would the coach trip cost a party of 12?

9 Mrs Gray bought one hundred 12p stamps. How much did she have to pay?

Money

division

1. Mary's father earns £120 for working a 40-hour week. How much does he earn per hour?

2. The bus fare into town is 8p. How many children could go into town by bus for £1.60?

3. How many twelvepenny stamps can be bought with thirty-six pence?

4. Joan paid £2.08 for four dozen eggs. How much would be the cost of one dozen eggs?

5. Fred paid £6.40 in rent every four weeks. How much is the rent per week?

6. Six people won a prize of £90 between them. How much would each person have?

7. A bag of five hundred 50p coins was exchanged for pound notes. How many pound notes were given in exchange?

8. If I paid the greengrocer £1.74 for 3 kg of apples, how much would 1 kg of apples cost?

9. Gail had saved £196. She spent one-quarter of this on a new radio. How much did the radio cost?

Money

mixed

1. Mary had 90p in her purse. If she bought 3 ninepenny stamps, how much did that leave in her purse?

2. Jack had £1.40 in his bank. His father gave him half as much again. How much did that make altogether?

3. My change from a five pound note was 1 fifty pence piece and 3 tenpenny pieces. How much had I spent?

4. How much change should I get if I buy three 12p stamps and give the shop assistant four tenpenny coins?

5. 25p, £2, £3, 17p Add the smallest two amounts, then divide your answer by three.

6. An electric light bulb costs 40p. What will be my change from £3 if I buy 6 bulbs?

7. The bus fare is 20p for adults and half price for children. How much would be the fare for 6 adults and 4 children?

8. A single ticket to Swansea cost £2.70; a return ticket cost £5.00 How much cheaper than two single tickets is one return?

9. John took one-quarter of his £5 savings from his money box. He bought a box of crayons which cost £1.22. How much money could he put back in his box?

Time
addition

1 Mary leaves for school at 8.15 a.m. If she spends 10 minutes walking and 10 minutes on a bus, when should she arrive at school?

2 David was born in 1968. How old was he in 1974, and how old was he in 1976?

3 Joy left home at 4.30 p.m. She travelled an hour by train and half an hour by bus to visit her friend. When did she arrive at her friend's house?

4 Susan caught 36-hour 'flu on Monday evening. When should she be better?

5 The football match was due to finish at 8.30 p.m.
Write down the actual finishing time if injury time amounted to ten minutes.

6 A clock chimed every fifteen minutes. If the first chime was heard at 7.00 a.m., write down the times of the next 4 chimes.

7 Lyn's birthday was on the 11th of October. Tom's was 12 days later. What was the date of Tom's birthday?

8 The 10.20 a.m. train left half an hour late. When did it leave?

9 Our grandfather clock was made in 1888. How old will it be in 1999?

Time
subtraction

1   Sam arrived half an hour early for the 11.45 train. At what time did he arrive?

2   Mary was born one week before St. Andrew's day which is the 30th of November. What date is Mary's birthday?

3   John finished his exam at 3.30 p.m. having written for $1\frac{1}{2}$ hours. At what time did he begin?

4   Write down the three leap years before 1980.

5   Tom's journey lasted 3 hours 40 minutes. Jack's lasted 2 hours 20 minutes. How much longer did Tom's journey take?

6   George was eight years old on the twelfth of January 1979. When was his fifth birthday?

7   Mrs Brown's bread took $\frac{1}{2}$ an hour to rise. If it had risen by 11.00 a.m., when had she put it to rise?

8   Sally's ninth birthday is on the 2nd of June. Robert is nine on the 4th of July. How many days older is Sally than Robert?

9   Father took the eggs out of the pan at 6 minutes past 10. They had been boiling for 4 minutes. At what time had they started to boil?

Time
multiplication

1 Rosemary says she sleeps for nine hours every night. How many hours is that each week?

2 Edward spends a total of 12 minutes every day brushing his teeth. How many hours and minutes is that in one week?

3 One page of sums took Gary 20 minutes to do. How many hours should he take to do six pages of sums?

4 If Father spends two hours every week cleaning the car, how many hours does he spend on the car in one year?

5 Ann works in the garden for 30 minutes every day. How many hours does she work in the garden in one week?

6 In the summer the school holidays last for seven weeks and two days. How many days' holiday is that?

7 A lighthouse beacon flashes once every 5 seconds. How many times is that in one minute?

8 Sally spends 1 hour 20 minutes with her Grandma every day. How much time does she spend with her Grandma in one week?

9 Twelve children each spend 10 minutes on the trampoline. How long do they spend on it in all?

Time
division

1. Our new baby has to be fed every 4 hours. How many times does she have to be fed in one day?

2. Three children borrow Jane's bike for $1\frac{1}{2}$ hours. If each child has an equal turn on the bike, how long will each turn be?

3. A leap year occurs every 4 years. 1968 was a leap year. How many leap years were there between 1969 and 1977?

4. How many weeks are there in one-quarter of a year?

5. The Easter holiday this year was 17 days long. How many weeks and days is that?

6. In 3 h 36 min Mother spends an equal amount of time on cooking, cleaning and washing up. How much time does she give to each activity?

7. A stove burns for 48 hours on six litres of oil. For how long will it burn on one litre?

8. From Monday to Friday Mr Jones spends a total of 10 hours travelling to work. How many hours does this amount to each day?

9. A razor blade lasts Father for 3 days. How many blades will he use in 3 weeks?

Time
mixed

1 Ann came home from school at 4.15 p.m. Father arrived $2\frac{1}{4}$ hours later. At what time did Father arrive?

2 Yesterday Andrew spent $1\frac{1}{2}$ hours painting the shed. Today he spent 20 minutes less than this on it. How much time is that altogether?

3 My train leaves at 11.5 a.m. If I have exactly 10 minutes to wait, what is the time now?

4 How many days are there altogether in the months of April, May, and June?

5 Buses arrive at the station every 20 minutes. The first one arrives at 6.00 a.m. When should the third one arrive?

6 Joan does 20 minutes' piano practice every day except Sunday. How many hours is that each week?

7 Peter's birthday is on the 21st of October. If today is the 7th of October, how many weeks are there till his birthday?

8 Debbie is 10 years old. Her father is now aged 37. How old was her father when Debbie was born?

9 Edward can hold his breath for three-quarters of a minute. How many seconds is that?

Length
addition

1 Monica sewed 80 cm of the curtain seam on Monday, and the remaining 120 cm on Tuesday. How long was the seam in metres?

2 Tom paints 1.40 m of the pole. Tracy paints 2 m and Joy paints 1.50 m. Find the total length of the pole they painted.

3 A book measures 21 cm by 14.5 cm. How far is it all around the edge?

4 John's rope measures 1.50 metres, but Mary's rope is 0.80 metres longer. How long is Mary's rope?

5 James cycles 3.3 km to see Bill and another 0.8 km to meet Simon. Find the total distance that he cycles.

6 Stephen is 1.4 m tall. The ceiling is 1.1 m above his head. What is the height from floor to ceiling?

7 Michael ran in the 800 m race and twenty minutes later he ran 400 m in the relay. How far did he run altogether?

8 Sue's sunflower was $2\frac{1}{2}$ m tall. If its height has increased by 800 cm, how tall is it now?

9 A desk which is 70 cm high is put on a table which is 95 cm high. What is the combined height of desk and table?

Length
subtraction

1 Richard is 1.25 m tall. His brother is 1.50 m tall. How much taller than Richard is his brother?

2 The distance all around a rectangle is 12 cm. The rectangle is 4 cm long. How wide is it?

3 The factory chimney was 128 m in height. The height of the church steeple was 30 metres less. How high was the steeple?

4 A van drove beneath a 2.5 m high bridge with 40 cm to spare. What was the height of the van?

5 A length of 1.80 m was sawn from a 5 m long plank of wood. What length was left?

6 600 m, 3000 m, 1 km, 4000 m. Take the shortest of these lengths from the longest.

7 The top of a 12 m flag staff is 9.8 m above the ground. What length of the flag staff is in the ground?

8 Tom's pencil measured 15 cm. After he had sharpened it, the pencil was 8 mm shorter. What length of pencil was left?

9 The 8-year olds had to run 60 m in the school sports, and the 5-year olds ran 25 m less. How far did the 5-year old children run?

Length
multiplication

1 Six 9 cm square tiles are laid end to end to cover a window sill. What length of window sill is covered?

2 The distance round a running track is 400 m. Jim runs six times round the track. How far does he run?

3 The length of one side of a square lawn is 5 metres. What is the distance all around the edge?

4 Tom is 1.20 m tall. The height of the classroom ceiling is four times his height. What is the height of the ceiling?

5 Ten copies of this book form a pile 3 cm high. How high would be a pile of 25 copies of the book?

6 John walks to school and back five days a week. If he walks $1\frac{1}{2}$ km each day, how far is that each week?

7 I need $2\frac{1}{2}$ m of curtain material for one window. How much material do I need for five windows the same size?

8 If ten 20 cm rods are laid end to end, what will be the total length in metres?

9 Jill's pace measures 40 cm. She takes nine paces to cross the lawn. How many metres wide is the lawn?

Length
division

1 The perimeter of a square rug is 3.20 m. What is the length of one side?

2 Simon's paces are 50 cm long. How many paces will he take to cross a $2\frac{1}{2}$ m path?

3 How many girls could be given a 30 cm length of hair ribbon from a 3 m roll?

4 My scarf is to be 126 cm long. If I knit 6 cm every day, how long will it take to knit the scarf?

5 Twenty-five school hymn books make a pile 50 cm high. How thick is each book?

6 Father takes the same route to work and back five days a week. The total distance he travels is 40 km. How far is it to work?

7 Kate swam a total of 120 m in the swimming gala. If the length of the pool was 20 m, how many lengths did she swim?

8 Andrew cycled 41 km in two hours at a steady speed. About how many kilometres each hour is that?

9 If a tree grew 36 cm in three years, about how much did it grow in one year?

Length
mixed

1 James has a 2 m curtain rod. He needs another rod half as long again. What length will this be?

2 How far is it all around a triangular field which has sides of 90 m, 60 m, and 80 m?

3 The distance between two doorposts is 158 cm. If a pair of doors are fitted, how wide will each door be?

4 Eight books are each 3.5 cm thick. If they are stacked one on the other, how high is the stack?

5 Jane is 1.40 m tall and her brother is 1.00 m tall. How many centimetres taller than her brother is Jane?

6 A pole cast a shadow twice its own length. If the shadow was 9.4 m long, how tall was the pole?

7 The perimeter of a rectangle is 11 cm. The two long sides have a total length of 10 cm. What is the width?

8 A tank measures 2 m by 2 m and 1 m deep. If it is half full of water, what is the depth of water?

9 How many 20 cm squares of wood could be cut from a plank 20 cm wide and 2 m long?

Weight
addition

1 A shopkeeper mixes 600 g of walnuts, 500 g of hazelnuts, 500 g of raisins and 400 g of sultanas. What is the total weight?

2 Mother added 400 g of sugar to 800 g of flour. Write down the combined weight in kilograms.

3 500 g, 5000 g, 50 kg, 3 kg Add the heaviest of these weights to the second heaviest.

4 Find the total weight of the following: 200 g margarine, 200 g sugar, 200 g oats, 400 g syrup, 500 g flour.

5 Mrs Green picked 7.5 kg of strawberries and her husband picked another 6.5 kg. What weight did they pick together?

6 Sheila is mixing powder paint. She uses 500 g of red and twice as much yellow. How many kilograms of powder paint has she used?

7 Julie weighs 23 kg and her brother weighs 39 kg. What do the scales read if both stand on together?

8 A tray contains two 50 g apples, two 100 g bananas, one 200 g orange, and one 400 g bunch of grapes. Find the total weight to the nearest kilogram.

9 Two lorries are each loaded with 1500 kg of coal. What is the total weight of this coal in tonnes?

Weight
subtraction

1 Mary weighs 32 kg. Jane is $4\frac{1}{2}$ kg lighter. How much does Jane weigh?

2 The shopkeeper said my apples weighed 20 g under two kilograms. What weight showed on the scales?

3 A sack of cement weighs 12 kg. If one-quarter of it is used, what weight is left in the sack?

4 Mother took $2\frac{1}{2}$ kg of apples on a picnic. She brought 800 g home. Write in grams the weight of apples that had been eaten.

5 Paul's mother is slimming. She has lost $7\frac{1}{2}$ kg in weight. She had weighed 60 kg. What is her weight now?

6 500 mg, 30 g, 2 g, 50 g. Subtract the lightest of these weights from the heaviest.

7 What is the difference in weight between a $1\frac{1}{2}$ kg bag of flour and an 800 g bag of beans?

8 Mr Brown is 9 kg heavier than his son. If Mr Brown weighs 68.5 kg, how heavy is his son?

9 In a joint of meat weighing 2.3 kg there is 250 g of bone. What is the weight of meat?

Weight
multiplication

1 A bag contains two hundred coins, each weighing 10 g. What is the total weight in kilograms of the coins?

2 Sue was four times as heavy as her dog. If the dog weighed 12.2 kg, what was Sue's weight to the nearest kilogram?

3 A shopkeeper orders one hundred 100 g packets of tea. What is the total weight in kilograms of this tea?

4 If one sack of potatoes weighs 15 kg, how much will 20 sacks weigh?

5 Each week the dustman carries about 8 kg of rubbish from our house. About how much will he carry away in one year?

6 One hundred children each brought about 250 g of fruit and vegetables for the Harvest Festival. About how many kilograms is that altogether?

7 How many one kilogram weights would be needed to balance twelve 500 g weights?

8 Bob delivered a 20 kg sack of potatoes to each of the six houses in the block. How many kilograms did he deliver altogether?

9 What would be the total weight in tonnes of ten 700 kg loads of wood?

Weight
division

1 The weight of fruit gums in a packet is 114 g. How many fruit gums are there in the packet if each weighs 3 g?

2 In a 100 kg sack of potatoes, one-quarter by weight are bad. What is the weight of the good potatoes?

3 Five washing machines have a total weight of half a tonne. How heavy is each machine?

4 A lorry is loaded with 2 tonnes of pet food in 25 kg sacks. How many sacks of pet food are on the lorry?

5 Sally divided 2 kg of sand equally between four trays. How many grams of sand did she put on each tray?

6 The weight of 30 pennies is 105 g. Work out the weight of one penny.

7 How many children could each have 30 g of toffees from a tin containing 660 g of toffees?

8 A van can carry $\frac{1}{2}$ tonne of meat. How many journeys must the van make to deliver $7\frac{1}{2}$ tonnes of meat?

9 On a lorry there are $1\frac{1}{2}$ tonnes of coal in 50 kg sacks. How many sacks of coal are on the lorry?

Weight
mixed

1 Joan ate half of a $\frac{1}{4}$ kg box of chocolates. Write, in grams, the weight of the chocolate left in the box.

2 Seed potatoes are sold in $2\frac{1}{2}$ kg bags. I need 9 kg. How many bags must I buy?

3 In jam-making, $\frac{3}{4}$ kg of sugar is used with every kilogram of fruit. If 4 kg of fruit is used, how much sugar is needed?

4 How much weight must Mrs White lose if she weighs 68 kg now and she wants to be 1 kg less than 60 kg?

5 Three 50 gram bars of chocolate are shared between two children. What weight of chocolate does each child get?

6 A pack of flour weighs 10 kg. How many more packs must be added to the nine I have to make up an order for 100 kg of flour?

7 Seven 600 g weights are needed to balance a bag of sand. What is the weight of the sand to the nearest kilogram?

8 Five children each get 800 g of clay from a 20 kg lump. What weight of clay is left?

9 A father weighs four times as much as his son. Together they weigh 100 kg. How much does each weigh?

Capacity
addition

1. Anne drank 500 ml of squash at the picnic. Sue drank half as much. How much did they drink altogether?

2. The water container was half full. James poured in $4\frac{1}{2}$ litres so that it was now full. How much did the container hold when full?

3. Add one-half of a litre to the total of these quantities: 500 ml, 2 litres, 1000 ml, 10 litres.

4. Mother mixed 500 ml of orange, 500 ml of lemon, and 600 ml of water in a jug. How many litres is that altogether?

5. John's father made 10 litres of wine. His uncle made twice that amount. How much wine was made in all?

6. Miss Ford bought 500 ml of red paint, 500 ml of yellow paint, 750 ml of green paint, and 1 litre of white paint. How much paint, to the nearest litre, did she buy altogether?

7. Tom was given 150 ml of medicine. His father was given three times this amount. What quantity is this in all?

8. Father mixed $4\frac{1}{2}$ litres of water with 500 ml of fertilizer. How much mixture did he make altogether?

9. Sally put 800 litres of water into the paddling pool, then John added 1100 litres. How much water is now in the pool?

Capacity
subtraction

1 If a car uses 168 litres of petrol in a month and a lorry uses 560 litres, how much more petrol does the lorry use?

2 In a café a four-litre container was filled with coffee. An hour later there was 1.5 litres left. How many litres had been drunk?

3 Six 200 ml cupfuls of milk are poured from a jug containing $1\frac{1}{2}$ litres. How much milk is left in the jug?

4 In a 120 litre mixture of weedkiller and water, one-third of it was weedkiller. How much of it was water?

5 Father had used one-quarter of the 60 litres of petrol that he bought. What quantity of petrol was left?

6 Miss Smith made 20 litres of lemonade for the school fête. If she sold three-quarters of it, how many litres were left?

7 700 ml, 2000 ml, 3 litres, 4000 ml Find the difference between the smallest of these amounts and the largest.

8 John drank 600 ml from his 2 litre flask. How much was left in the flask?

9 Half the contents of a 15 litre container was poured into a large bowl. What quantity was left in the container?

Capacity
multiplication

1 Our heater burns 500 ml of oil every day. How many litres of oil will it burn in one week?

2 Each of six children was given 250 ml of milk. How many litres is that?

3 A petrol tanker delivered 4000 litres of petrol to each of four garages. How much petrol did it deliver altogether?

4 A nurse filled fifty cups with water. She put 250 ml in each. How many litres of water did she use?

5 6000 ml, 40 litres, 4000 ml, 7500 ml. Multiply the largest of these amounts by four.

6 Father's watering can holds 8.3 litres. He filled it six times to water the garden. How much water, to the nearest litre, did he use?

7 James had to take a 5 ml spoonful of medicine four times a day for ten days. How much medicine did he take altogether?

8 How many one-litre bottles could be filled from twenty 750 ml jugfuls?

9 What is the total capacity of six 4.5 litre containers?

Capacity
division

1 Six full bottles of water are needed to fill our 9 litre watering can. How much does each bottle hold?

2 12 litres, 2400 ml, 16 litres, 320 ml. Divide the greatest of these amounts by eight.

3 Simon takes 210 ml of medicine in one week. How much does he take each day?

4 A petrol tanker delivers equal quantities of petrol to three different garages. If a total of 15 000 litres is delivered, how much does each garage receive?

5 Mother divides 2 litres of squash equally between ten glasses. How many millilitres does she pour into each glass?

6 In five days Uncle Fred uses 1800 litres of water in his garden. If the daily amounts are equal, how much does he use each day?

7 Miss Cook divided the $2\frac{1}{2}$ litres of paint between ten jars. How much paint did she put in each jar?

8 One-quarter of the 5 litre can of engine oil was put in Uncle Tom's car. How many millilitres is that?

9 How many 2 litre bottles of wine can be filled from a barrel containing one thousand litres?

Capacity
mixed

1 I need 250 ml of paint to cover one door. How many litres of paint should I buy to give four doors two coats of paint?

2 Mrs. Jones uses about the same amount of water in her kitchen each day. If she uses 1500 litres in three days, how much will she use in one week?

3 A fish tank will hold 22 litres. If the tank is one-quarter full, how much water is in it?

4 George drank 750 ml of milk every day. Sam drank twice this amount. How much did Sam drink in a week?

5 My car uses 20 litres of petrol each week. Jill's moped uses 2 litres of petrol each day. How much more petrol does my car use in one week?

6 A kettle holds 3 litres. If a teapot holds 750 ml, how many times can it be filled from one kettleful of water?

7 Four children were each given 400 ml of orange juice. How many one-litre bottles of juice had to be opened?

8 One-quarter of Mother's home-made wine filled 5 two-litre bottles. How much wine did she make altogether?

9 A can holds 15 litres of paraffin. When ten litres have been used, what fraction of the 15 litres is then left?